THE CEMETERY GANG

THE CEMETERY GANG

Sylvia Landuyt

Illustrated by Kimb Beers

VANTAGE PRESS
New York

FIRST EDITION

Copyright © 1996 by Sylvia Landuyt

Published by Vantage Press, Inc.
516 West 34th Street, New York, New York 10001

Manufactured in the United States of America
ISBN: 0-533-11779-8

Library of Congress Catalog Card No.: 96-90026

0 9 8 7 6 5 4 3 2 1

To my soul mate, Dick, our six unique children, six wonderful grandchildren, one special great-grandson, and to all fellow seekers of God and our purpose here on Earth.

A special thanks to Kimb Beers, the illustrator; our grandson, Ryan Wagner, for the cover printing; Pat, who bailed me out with his camera-ready spelling corrections; and especially to God, who has given me my gifts.

OCTOBER, 1964

WE HAVE BEEN WANTING TO TELL
THIS STORY FOR A LONG TIME, BUT
WE WERE AFRAID NO ONE WOULD
BELIEVE US.

ALMOST TWO MONTHS LATER, AFTER
THANKSGIVING, WE BEGAN TO
WORRY ABOUT FORGETTING
EXACTLY WHAT HAPPENED SO WE
DECIDED TO WRITE IT DOWN.

YOU MAY BE THE FIRST PERSON
TO READ THIS!

1

THERE ARE SIX OF US: THERESA, MIKE, ANNIE, ROSE, ROB AND GERRY. WE ARE ALL IN THE SEVENTH GRADE AT PARKE MIDDLE SCHOOL AND LIVE IN THE SAME NEIGHBORHOOD.

EVER SINCE FOURTH GRADE, AFTER SUPPER, WHEN OUR HOMEWORK WAS DONE, WE'D RIDE OUR BIKES A FEW BLOCKS AWAY THROUGH THE WOODS TO THIS SMALL GRAVEYARD. THAT'S WHY WE CALL OURSELVES THE CEMETERY GANG.

THE CEMETERY HAS ABOUT
FIFTEEN TOMBSTONES AND
TWO DOZEN OR SO BIG OLD TREES,
SOME WITH HUGE TRUNKS AND
GNARLY ROOTS. THERE IS EVEN
A GIANT WEEPING WILLOW.

SOMETIMES WE'D PLAY GAMES
LIKE TAG OR HIDE AND SEEK OR
JUST SIT ON A TOMBSTONE AND
TALK.

ONCE IN A WHILE WE'D MAKE UP
STORIES ABOUT THE PEOPLE WHOSE
NAMES WERE ON THE TOMBSTONES,
AT LEAST THE ONES WE COULD
READ. SOME OF THEM WERE OLD
AND HARD TO MAKE OUT.

WE COULD FIGURE OUT ABOUT
SIX OF THEM CLEARLY. THEY
WERE "ABIGAIL PIERCE 1891-
1933," "HENRY GREENSLEEVES
1919-1947," "JACOB SIMON 1894-
1928," "EMMA KERR 1900-1955,"
"EILEEN O'SHEA 1903-1960" AND
"WARREN J. FREDERICK 1902-
1953."

ON OCTOBER 1, 1964 IT WAS A
BEAUTIFUL FALL NIGHT. THE
MOON WAS SO BIG AND BRIGHT IT
ALMOST SEEMED LIKE DAY!

THE MOONLIGHT SHOWN THROUGH
THE TREES AND MADE SHADOWS
ON THE TOMBSTONES. THERE
WERE A MILLION STARS OUT. YOU
COULD HEAR THE WIND
WHISTLING THROUGH THE
LEAVES ALMOST MAKING AN
EERY SOUND!

It was a perfect time for telling ghost stories.

ANNIE STARTED AND WE ALL
took turns. EACH STORY WAS
SCARIER THAN THE FIRST AND
BEFORE YOU KNEW IT, WE
WERE SHAKING AND LOOKING
OVER OUR SHOULDERS WITH
GOOSEBUMPS ALL OVER!

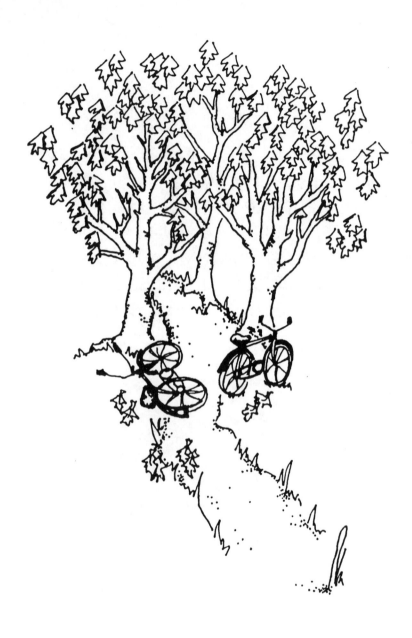

WE KNEW WE SHOULD GO HOME
BUT WE WERE FROZEN STIFF
WITH FEAR.

THE PATH HOME WAS THROUGH
THE WOODS AND NONE OF US WAS
BRAVE ENOUGH TO BE THE
FIRST TO GO FOR OUR BIKES,
WHICH WERE ACROSS THE
GRAVEYARD THROUGH ALL
THE TOMBSTONES.

AS WE WERE TRYING TO GATHER
UP OUR COURAGE TO MAKE A
MOVE, THERESA WHISPERED IN
A FRIGHTENED VOICE, "OH NO!"

HER EYES WERE AS WIDE AS
COULD BE. THEY LOOKED LIKE
THEY WERE READY to POP
OUT OF HER HEAD!

SHE POINTED TO ABIGAIL'S
GRAVE AND AS WE TURNED TO
LOOK OUR MOUTHS DROPPED
OPEN AND OUR FACES TURNED
WHITE AS A SHEET.

OVER ABIGAIL'S GRAVE WAS A
GOLDEN, WHITE BRILLIANT LIGHT
IN THE SHAPE OF A WOMAN.
HER LONG HAIR WAS STREAMING
BEHIND HER IN THE WIND.

AS SHE SAW SHE HAD ALL OF
OUR ATTENTION, SHE BEGAN
TO SPEAK.

HER VOICE WAS JUST LIKE THE
RUSTLING OF THE LEAVES, MAKING
A MUSIC-LIKE SOUND.

SHE CALLED OUT EACH OF OUR
NAMES AND THEN SHE SAID,
"MY FRIENDS AND I HAVE BEEN
WATCHING YOU PLAY FOR THREE
YEARS AND WE HAVE GROWN TO
LOVE YOU.

WE ASKED GOD FOR PERMISSION
to LEt YOU SEE US SO tHAT
WE COULD tELL YOU OUR OWN
STORIES. WE tHINk YOU COULD
LEARN SOMEtHING VERY
IMPORtANt.

DON'T BE AFRAID. WE WOULD NEVER HURT YOU. WE ARE YOUR FRIENDS. JUST RELAX AND LISTEN VERY CAREFULLY.

I LIVED A VERY LONG TIME AGO,
BEFORE THERE WERE AUTOMOBILES.
I PLAYED SOME OF THE SAME
GAMES YOU HAVE BEEN PLAYING
HERE WITH YOUR FRIENDS.

I WAS BORN ON AN INDIAN
RESERVATION. MY INDIAN NAME
WAS "TONWEYA" WHICH MEANS
"RIDES AHEAD." WHEN I WAS FIVE
YEARS OLD I LEARNED TO RIDE
HORSES BAREBACK AND WANTED
TO TRAIN THEM WHEN I GREW
UP.

WHEN MY PARENTS DIED, I WAS
ADOPTED BY THE PIERCE FAMILY
AND GIVEN THE NAME ABIGAIL.
WE MOVED TO A SMALL TOWN
WHERE MY FATHER WAS PASTOR
OF THE LOCAL CHURCH.

I NEVER RODE HORSES AGAIN
AND AFTER MANY YEARS, I
FORGOT ABOUT MY CHILDHOOD
DREAM.

AS ABIGAIL SPOKE, SHE SEEMED
TO BECOME BRIGHTER.

WE HAD TO SHIELD OUR EYES,
AND WHEN SHE WAS DONE TELLING
HER STORY, WE LOOKED UP INTO
THE SILENCE AND THERE WERE
NOW SIX SHIMMERING LIGHTS OF
ALL DIFFERENT COLORS SHINING
OVER ALL SIX OF THE GRAVES.

ABIGAIL SAID, "THESE ARE YOUR OTHER FRIENDS. THEY WOULD LIKE TO SAY A FEW WORDS TO YOU TOO."

JACOB SPOKE NEXT. HIS VOICE WAS LOW AND SAD.

"I WAS BORN IN 1889. MY FATHER WAS THE TEACHER IN OUR TOWN. EVER SINCE I WAS YOUNG, I USED TO MAKE UP COSTUMES AND PRETEND I WAS A FAMOUS EXPLORER OR A CAPTAIN OF A SHIP ON THE HIGH SEAS."

"I LOVED TO ENTERTAIN MY
BROTHER AND SISTER AND THEIR
FRIENDS. AS I GOT OLDER PEOPLE
TOLD ME I WAS FOOLISH AND
SHOULD BE SOMETHING MORE
SERIOUS SO I COULD EARN A

GOOD LIVING. I LET MY DREAM
OF BEING AN ACTOR GO. AND,
SOMEWHERE INSIDE ME, A LIGHT
WENT OUT."

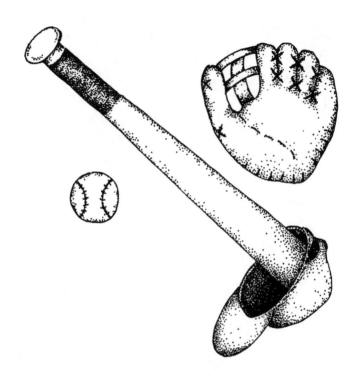

A DEEP VOICE NEXT TO JACOB
BEGAN TO SPEAK.

"WITH A NAME HENRY GREENSLEEVES,
I WAS TEASED AND NEVER ASKED
TO PLAY BASEBALL WITH THE REST
OF THE GUYS EVEN THOUGH I
WAS THE BEST RUNNER AND
PITCHER THERE WAS."

"I GAVE UP TOO EASILY. I NEVER
TRIED TO BECOME THE BASEBALL
PLAYER I DREAMED OF."

THEN EMMA CRIED OUT, "I KNOW,
I KNOW!"

"I WAS SO SHY. I THOUGHT SOMEWHERE
DEEP INSIDE I WASN'T GOOD ENOUGH
OR THAT PEOPLE WOULD MAKE FUN
OF ME, SO I NEVER TRIED OUT FOR
THE SCHOOL PLAYS OR BECAME THE
SINGER I ALWAYS WANTED TO BE
IN MY HEART."

"WELL, I HAD AN EXCITING LIFE," BOOMED WARREN. "ALTHOUGH IT WASN'T WHAT I PLANNED."

"I RODE ALL OVER THE COUNTRY IN A COVERED WAGON, SO I NEVER REALLY WENT TO SCHOOL PAST FIFTH GRADE. I WAS A BLACKSMITH AND A COWBOY."

"EVERY CHANCE I GOT THOUGH, I WOULD READ ALL THE BOOKS I COULD GET MY HANDS ON. READING WAS MY GREAT LOVE BUT I NEVER FINISHED SCHOOL OR BECAME A TEACHER OF THOSE BOOKS I SO LOVED."

THE SOFT LIFTING VOICE OF
EILEEN SAID, "MY FAMILY OWNED
THE GENERAL STORE IN TOWN.
I LEARNED TO PLAY THE PIANO
WHEN I WAS JUST A GIRL. I WAS
HAPPIEST WHEN I WAS LOST IN
THE MUSIC I PLAYED."

"AS I GOT OLDER, I HAD TO HELP
OUT IN THE STORE AND SOON WAS
WORKING 12 TO 16 HOURS A DAY.
THE PIANO BECAME QUIET AND
DUSTY AND THEN I MOVED AWAY TO
A NEW TOWN AND NEVER PLAYED
AGAIN."

EVEN THOUGH THE CEMETERY WAS
BRILLIANT WITH THE LIGHTS OF OUR
SPIRIT FRIENDS, SOMETHING INSIDE
OUR HEARTS FELT VERY SAD AND
WE DIDN'T KNOW WHY.

THEN ABIGAIL SPOKE AGAIN. SHE
SAID, "EACH ONE OF US HAD A
PASSION TO DO SOMETHING WE
REALLY LOVED AND YET EACH ONE
OF US LET THAT DREAM DIE."

"ALL OF OUR DREAMS ARE BURIED
HERE WITH US IN THIS CEMETERY."

"WE WERE SENT to GIVE YOU A MESSAGE. YOU ARE ALL to KNOW AND NEVER FORGET THAT GOD GIVES EVERY PERSON MANY GIFTS. SOME GIFTS ARE EASY to SEE, LIKE A TALENT SUCH AS SINGING OR BEING ATHLETIC."

"SOME GIFTS YOU HAVE to TAKE
NOTICE OF, LIKE A SPECIAL INTEREST
IN SCIENCE, LANGUAGE OR IN HELPING
PEOPLE. THEN THERE ARE GIFTS
WE FORGET to NOTICE AND DON't
EVEN REALIZE OR THINK OF AS
SPECIAL, BUT WE ALL HAVE SEVERAL
OF THESE AND THEY ARE JUST AS
IMPORTANT AS THE OTHERS."

"THESE GIFTS ARE BEING EXCEPTIONALLY
KIND, VERY ORGANIZED, HAVING A VERY
LOVING HEART OR WHEN GENEROSITY
COMES NATURALLY TO YOU."

"OH, THERE ARE MANY, MANY MORE!
YOU SEE, WHEN GOD GIVES YOU YOUR
GIFTS, HE EXPECTS YOU TO USE
THEM AND SHARE THEM WITH OTHERS.
SO MANY PEOPLE HAVE NOT REALIZED
THAT."

"DID YOU KNOW, THE MORE YOU
USE YOUR GIFTS, THE BIGGER AND
BETTER THEY GET?"

"THE MORE YOU USE AND RECOGNIZE
YOUR GIFTS, THE HAPPIER YOU WILL
BE. IF EVERYONE WOULD USE
WHATEVER GIFTS THEY HAVE
THE WORLD WOULD BE A BETTER
PLACE."

"THE MOST WONDERFUL THING IS
THAT EVERYONE, EVERY PERSON
ON EARTH HAS "GIFTS." IT'S
OUR JOB TO FIND THE SPECIALNESS
IN OTHERS AND TO TELL THEM.
IT'S ALSO OUR JOB TO RECOGNIZE
OUR OWN GIFTS AND BE BRAVE
ENOUGH TO USE THEM!"

THEN ALL OUR SPIRIT FRIENDS
SPOKE TOGETHER. THE CEMETERY
WAS FILLED WITH A SHIMMERING
BRIGHTNESS AND ALL THE COLORS
OF THE RAINBOW, AS THEY SAID,
"FIND YOUR GIFTS, EACH ONE AS
IMPORTANT AS THE NEXT, GIVEN
TO YOU TO USE, NOT HIDE."

"OUR DREAMS ARE BURIED HERE
IN THE CEMETERY. THEY WERE
NEVER USED BECAUSE WE
WERE AFRAID."

"ALWAY REMEMBER WHAT WE
HAVE TOLD YOU HERE."

"ALWAYS REMEMBER ! "

THEN.THEY BEGAN to DISAPPEAR
ONE BY ONE UNTIL IN THE BLINK
OF AN EYE WE WERE THERE,
JUST THE SIX OF US, ALL ALONE
AGAIN.

It SEEMED AS IF WE StOOD THERE
StILL AS A StONE FOR HOURS
AND YET NO tIME HAD PASSED At
ALL.

NO ONE SPOKE. FINALLY, WE
BEGAN to LOOK At EACH OTHER
AND WONDER, "DID WE ALL HEAR
AND SEE THE SAME tHING? WAS
It A DREAM?"

WE KNEW WE WERE LATE
AND HAD TO HURRY HOME BUT
THAT SOMEHOW WE WOULD NEVER
BE THE SAME AGAIN.

WE PROMISED EACH OTHER THAT
WE WOULDN'T TELL ANYONE
ABOUT WHAT WE SAW OR HEARD
UNTIL WE HAD A CHANCE TO TALK
ABOUT IT.

THAT'S WHY WE'RE TELLING
YOU. THIS IS THE MESSAGE.

"FIND YOUR GIFTS, USE THEM,
BE BRAVE AND DON'T EVER
GIVE UP!"

ALWAYS REMEMBER, ALWAYS,
YOUR FRIENDS,

THE CEMETERY GANG

...AND TO OUR SPECIAL FRIENDS...

WE DIDN'T FORGET!

OCTOBER 1, 1994

THERESA   JOURNALIST AND
              FREELANCE WRITER

GERRY   GOLF PROFESSIONAL

ROSE   CONCERT PIANIST

MIKE   SCIENCE TEACHER AND
              BASEBALL COACH

ROB   PRIEST

ANNIE   SALES MANAGER AND
              LISTENER

ANNIE COULD LISTEN SO HARD SHE COULD
HEAR YOU WITH HER HEART... AND THAT
COULD BE THE BIGGEST GIFT OF ALL !\